Molecatcher

Jeff Nicholls

Molecatcher

A guide to traditional molecatching methods

Matador
9 De Montfort Mews
Leicester LE1 7FW, UK
Tel: (+44) 116 255 9311 / 9312
Email: books@troubador.co.uk
Web: www.troubador.co.uk/matador

First editionn 2004
Second edition 2006

ISBN 1 905237 76 6

Typeset in 10pt Stempel Garamond by Troubador Publishing Ltd, Leicester, UK
Printed in the UK by The Cromwell Press Ltd, Trowbridge, Wilts, UK

Matador is an imprint of Troubador Publishing Ltd

Molecatcher is dedicated to the molecatchers of the United Kingdom, and especially to those that have gone before me:

John Anderson, James Birkett, Tony Bowrain, Bill Pop Bowles, Andrew Burt, William Burrell, Thomas Buston, Richard Condor, John Couperthwaite, Peter Couperthwaite, Robert Couperthwaite, William Couperthwaite, John Currie, Samuel Dixon, James Drury, Robert Dumville, James Greatorex, Isaac Hewitt, David Imrie, Robert Johnston, George Keeler, John Keeler, Robert Keeler, Thomas Keeler, William Keeler, Thomas Kinnear, Kames McIntosh, John McGregor, William Monkman, Joseph Moody, Thomas Mounsey, John Murray, William Newman, Todd Nicholls, William Orr, Arthur Randell, John Reid, M Revely, Thomas Sellers, John Sheriff, Robert Sloan, George Smith, Charles Tailor, Alfred Taylor, Richard Taylor, William Thurlow, Thomas Turner, Frank Weale, Francis White, James Wilkinson, Matthew Wilkinson, Leonard Winn

and to John Newton Duffus, mole trap maker

Contents

Introduction

Since I have been catching moles, Concorde has made her first and final flight – aeronautical technology that was never bettered during her lifetime. Mole catching is also a method that has never been bettered since man first began to try and control this rarely seen creature. New technology has inspired many to compete with the old ways, but modern techniques have yet to offer an honest and respected means of getting rid of this common garden foe.

Like myself, many people have learned to catch moles hands-on, aided by instinct or a fascination for the mole. For me it has been a long scholarship, one that always seems to throw up new challenges. In this book, I have tried to explain the basic techniques of molecatching. The methods used are not set in stone, but hopefully these pages will enlighten those who also wish to acquire enough understanding of the mole to successfully catch them, and thus be called 'Molecatcher'.

There are two main reasons for writing this book. The first is obvious – you need to control moles. The second reason is a more selfish one – I would like you to learn ways of catching moles that give you an awareness of your quarry, using methods that are humane and effective, yet which have changed little in years.

Modern control methods are under constant scrutiny so that unnecessary suffering is not caused, and some such methods will rightly fade away. By all means consider all the methods of mole control available, but be aware of the consequences of these techniques on the mole, and the wider environment.

This book is intended as a practical guide to catching moles in the most humane and effective way possible, but it also serves to warn against employing cruel and expensive control methods that can cause more damage than good.

I wish you luck in your forthcoming battle with the mole!

Jeff Nicholls
April 2006

1

An introduction to molecatching

Molecatching is without a doubt a tradition that is fast fading into the mists of time. Molecatchers are no longer seen to wonder across fields or down shady lanes, bags on their shoulders and not a care in the world! Life for them is slow, no one to correct or instruct them, as only an isolated few have the knowledge to be called 'Molecatcher'. Yes, there are people who can catch the occasional mole, and it is often claimed that gardeners are as good as any molecatcher, but what skills are necessary before one can truly earn the name 'Molecatcher'?

Molecatchers catch moles anywhere and everywhere. Gardeners only catch in the gardens in which they work, in soil that rarely changes and locations that dictate little. A molecatcher will visit many locations where not only features and soil but also general conditions make many demands on the mole, all of which reflect on his skill and knowledge.

Nowadays pest control companies undertake mole control, but how many in today's economic market can claim to offer the results and service of the traditional molecatcher? Traditional molecatchers get paid by results. Historically, NO Mole meant NO Pay, and for centuries molecatchers have had to produce a mole as proof of the completed task and to receive payment. Most of today's disposal methods only offer that person's word that the mole has been removed – should another mole appear then there is no way of knowing if it is the same mole or another one.

1

Molecatching is in my opinion without doubt the most humane way to be rid of mole. I find it strange that in today's world so many inhumane attacks are aimed at the poor mole. We often proudly claim to be green and environmentally friendly, that is until a mole appears in the lawn. Then the list of substances that are pushed, poked and pumped into the mole's environment is endless, and the results? Well, nothing guaranteed. Mole has to spend all day dodging this, squeezing past that, and having to put up with all kinds of obnoxious smells.

Sometimes so much environmental effluent is stuffed down into the mole's home that a small holiday is taken, as much energy will be needed to dig new tunnels in the only remaining part of the prized lawn not to have been destroyed in man's efforts and desperation to be rid of this little man in black.

A molecatcher's traps

Molecatchers have always used traps, and today is no exception. I have often heard people cringe at the word 'trap'. This reaction probably exists as very few traps are seen in the shops, or in the media such as television or radio. Traps conjure up visions of large metal devices that tear off limbs and prolong suffering prior to death, but this is not the case. Traps catch by design, and are passed for use by the relevant authorities to carry out the task required.

Only mole traps can be used in the mole environment. Many traps have been – and rightly so – banned, as they have been used to kill, maim and torture many targeted and non-targeted species, including humans. The definition of the word trap – "to deceive or ensnare" – does nothing to help in today's language. Perhaps if we changed the definition found in the dictionary to "A quick and effective method of control", then people would find traps less repellent. Of course, it is important to remember that traps will only be effective and safe when used properly.

So how has molecatching changed over the years?

Molecatching has changed very little over the years. We know that moles plagued the Roman Empire from earthenware pots excavated from roman sites. These earthenware pots were used as traps, buried in the mole runs and part filled with water, Mole would fall in and drown. Whether this was the work of molecatchers all those years ago we may never know.

The buried pot method was used until recently all around the country, possibly all round the world. As time moved on, so has molecatching, and devices with moving parts were employed. The first real mole traps were born. These devices have changed little; the principals have remained the same to this day in the fact that some part of it had to be buried in the ground.

Earthenware pots progressed to clay barrel traps- a tube made from coarse earthenware which was a mixture of clay and ground up fired pots known as grog. The traps were made from a mould and although many molecatchers would have made their own the local potter was always to hand. These clay barrel traps took mole catching forward but they were easily broken under foot by both animal and man. The harsh conditions in which these traps were put to work also demanded a better material. Another traditional craft in the village was the solution to the problem – the wheelwright. Cart wheels were required to withstand extreme work loads in all weathers and very soon the molecatchers were using wooden barrels to replace the weaker clay. The wheel hubs were made from elm, a timber that is strong but more important resilient to moisture. Its strength enabled a metal spring to be stapled to it allowing for the bent mole sticks that powered the clay traps to be discarded. A compact self powered mole trap became available. The wheelwright or sometimes the bodger like the potter could provide the body of a mole trap for the molecatcher but the costs of these crafts-men dug deep into the molecatchers hard acquired money. Many of the

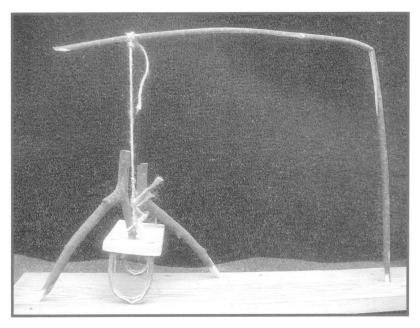

A traditional wooden mole trap

molecatchers of yesteryear continued to make their own traps with many a cold night being spent near the fire making traps from materials collected from the copse. These home made traps were very similar to the metal half-barrel traps I use today. Most home made traps were constructed from a piece of wood, two small hazel sticks, a twig for a nose peg and a length of string.

The piece of wood needed to be approximately 6 inches [150mm] x 2 inches [50 mm]. The thickness was not important but rarely exceeded three quarters of an inch or 20mm. This was to form the top or roof of the trap and five holes was drilled in it. One at each corner and one in the middle to hold the nose peg also known as a mumble pin. The personal touch was added here with notches cut and individual marks. When I first made my own I would carve a pattern around the edge.

4

The hazel sticks had to be no more than the thickness of a pencil and no more than a length of one. These are whittled down using a sharp knife to the soft centre core, which when scraped out provides a neat groove for the string to sit in. These sticks then required bending to form the loops that would hold the strings and form the legs the trap rested on. Steam from a boiling kettle or pan was applied to the middle of the sticks until they became pliable, or by soaking them in water. Slowly they could then be bent to the shape of a horseshoe. The use of a few nails and a block of wood would hold the sticks in this shape until they dried; some bent them round a pole. Once dry, the stick is cut to the size needed to allow the mole to pass through. This was about two and half inches [60mm], allowing a little that will be located in the piece of wood when it's all put together. The sticks locate in the four corner drilled holes and glue holds them tight. The string is threaded down one corner hole, squeezing past the stick, and is then pushed up out the other hole at the opposite corner. A knot is tied and the resulting loop is what catches the mole. With the other end of the string the same is carried out on the other end of the trap. The trap then consisted of a loop of string at each end, which was set in the natural grooves of the sticks. The string loops tied at each end of the piece of string meant that when the middle of the string was pulled, both loops operated upwards. (Some molecatchers used a copper wire to form these loops instead of string.)

This was the finished trap, but it still had to be powered. This was achieved like its fore-runner the clay barrel trap, known as a *mole stick*. This stick, or often sticks, needed to be flexible, so willow or another suitable wood was used. Allowing for the depth of a mole run the trap was to be set, another piece of string was tied central to the string containing the two loops. A tail on the knot used to join these strings together had another stop knot tied in it at the end. This tail was pushed through the middle hole in the piece of wood and held in by the nose peg or mumble pin. At this point the trap could be suspended by this new piece of string without the loops being disturbed. Only when the mumble pin is removed would the string move upwards, pulling the looped string with it. The trap was set in the run and held in place by two sticks cut as pegs. These pegs resisted the constant upward pull of the mole stick. The mole stick was pushed into the ground and bent over the trap site. The central string was tied to it, the mumble pin held tight and the pegs held it down.

When the mole passed through the wooden loops and pushed the nose peg free, the bend in the mole stick was free to return to its original upright position, thus pulling the string loops up with it and catching the mole. The mole was only held up against the wooden top or roof. The old molecatcher would set his traps and wait patiently for a bent stick to jerk up, indicating a catch. The molecatcher would rush over and collect the prize, for we must remember that no mole meant no pay.

These traditional traps were difficult to set, but molecatchers who did it all day and every day found it easy. Those who didn't practice couldn't do it, all of which added to the mystery of molecatching.

Many days were spent in this way by a certain young molecatcher (me), sitting under a tree with a comic and soft drink waiting for it all to happen. Then up would spring a stick showing a catch, and hopefully I'd get the four shillings (20p) payment. Four shillings was a fair payment considering that other young lads potato picking received five shillings (25p) a week

The old traps were set using a mole spud. This is a small square spade set at one end of a long handle, about 4 feet (1.2m) in length, with a metal spike fixed at the other end. The spike was used to drive a hole in the ground to hold the mole stick, having already dug the mole run to set the trap with the spade. The length of this tool saved a lot of kneeling and bending.

The clay and elm barrel traps showed certain disadvantages in comparison with the home made mole trap. It was not long before molecatchers were cutting the elm barrels in half to make two traps. These could still be used with a metal spring stapled to them, and they became known as *half barrel traps*. The metal spring caused more soil to be disturbed when used at certain depths of runs, unlike the traps still powered by a mole stick. However, the larger size and power of the metal spring meant that a mole when caught was held firm, so a molecatcher knew that to return to a sprung trap would secure the mole well. (The mole catching years using these traps powered by a mole stick cannot claim to be humane, as the mole was often left to die slowly held by a copper wire and the force from a willow branch.)

The molecatchers, being very shrewd characters, soon sought to replace the barrel traps with the half barrels, but the problem of powering them continued to be an issue. They had to return to the mole sticks when using homemade traps, unless they had the ability to turn their own and fix metal springs.

A traditional clay barrel trap

The molecatchers who used these traps knew their secrets, the mystery behind them. Only the gifted could ensure a wage from their use. The secret of these early traps was that clay and timber are porous. Porous it would absorb any scent or smell of humans, which would alert the mole to possible danger.

Molecatchers kept these traps free of human scent by handling them only after removing any sweat or moisture from their own hands with dry dirt.

Generations of molecatchers earned their living using these clay traps. From the late 1800's to the early 1900's, molecatchers were, on average, paid 12 shillings and six pence (62.5p) a season by farmers and estate owners to rid them of moles. These crafty old catchers, who made a lucrative living using their knowledge, were often paid a penny a tail for an individual catch, as the landowner was pleased to be rid of the little pest.

However, the molecatcher had not finished with his trade, because from each mole carefully tucked in the pocket he would remove the skins, dry them and sell them to London fur traders, or to a local plumber (who used them to wipe pipe joints) for six pence (2.5p) each. One molecatching family to use clay traps was the Turner family from Buckinghamshire The Turner family was obviously very good at this trade; at the turn of the century, Tom Turner caught enough moles in one season to pay the princely sum of £40 for his house. The clay traps the Turners used were often stolen by poachers, who saw an easy payday should a mole be present. The stolen traps were often of little use to the poachers, as they knew none of the secrets to setting them.

One man found the solution to the molecatcher's dilemma of a compact, self-powered trap. Born on the 20th April 1864 in Dundee, Scotland, John Newton Duffus was both a shepherd who, like two of his sons John and Alexander, turned his hands to molecatching. In 1920/21. He, along with another son, Laurie, an engineer, devised a

A spear trap

self-contained trap with two springs to catch from either direction, or two moles. It was far more advanced then anything at that time. It was compact, constructed from metal, could be used in any location and it was simple to set. It provided the molecatchers with a new weapon in the battle for mole control. John Newton Duffus, or Jake as he was called by friends and family, took his last breath in Eassie just to the north-west of Dundee. He will never be forgotten, as still in our world of computer plastic the Duffus half barrel trap, as it became fondly known, is still available. In 1958 the patent was sold to David Jolly, who continued to hand make them until 1992. The greatest tribute that can be made is to copy – internationally, John or David's trap is still copied today, but whatever the trap makers of tomorrow bring, the Duffus half barrel trap will always remain a part of molecatching history.

Many other trap manufacturers were keen to supply mole traps and produced many different types made from metal which followed the same principal as the old home made and barrel traps, all, that is, apart from the *Spear* or *Guillotine* trap, which was probably the most humane of all the traps used on moles. Again, it was all metal, very powerful in operation, and would kill either by the shear force at which it descended on its victim, or by piecing the mole's body with six four-and-a-half inch [120mm] spikes. This trap could not be used in deeper mole runs, but was ideal when a mole was working shallow (when the ground is raised or tunnelled just below the surface).

To set Spear or Guillotine traps, the roof of the mole run was crushed with the foot. The trap was pushed down into the ground, ensuring that the two main spikes straddled the run. It was pushed down to a depth so that the now flat roof of the mole's run was in contact with the release plate. The trap was sprung when mole came along the run and pushed the collapsed roof back up. The plate would release the spring, sending it down to its original position, thrusting the spikes into the run directly below. This is not a trap for the novice! This trap is obvious in use, and would rarely be used in deeper runs due to the difficulty in its operation. As with the modern traps today, metal is non-absorbent so the need to disguise any human scent is not necessary – but they still need to be kept away from unnecessary contaminants.

Molecatching fast became a private knowledge. The demand for mole-catching by landowners bought about territories, with each molecatcher prepared to fight to retain a lucrative estate. Travelling molecatchers would have areas they regularly worked, and at one time the mole-catcher was the envy of many. The proof of their skills was displayed on fence posts and gates for all to see, especially the squire or farmer, as proof for the payment they received. It was a skill that was cloaked further in mystery with their decline – a father may pass down the knowledge to a son to ensure an income for the family, but to share the knowledge was to divide the earnings.

So if these custodians of the countryside had it so good, where did they

A selection of different types of mole traps

come from, and where have they gone?

There were many changes to British agriculture towards the end of the 1700s, and the first part of the 1800s, from the demand to feed an ever increasing population. This demand for food was met by new farming techniques, crop rotation, land reclamation, new crops and higher numbers of stock animals. This new, efficient farming produced wealthy farmers who had already (with the implementation of the Enclosure Act in 1801) taken the strips of land from the peasants. New mechanized farming by horse, and shortly after steam, reduced the labour requirements. Along side all these changes, industry was also increasing, with better roads and railways making it possible for the now plentiful produce to be sent to the ever growing towns. Farming communities were forced to follow and to work in industry, exchanging the fresh smell of hay for the foul taste of progress. Very soon, more people were living in the towns than in the country. Those that stayed lived a life of hardship and poverty, many became the victims of the Poor Act, and the lists of the workhouse unions contain many names bearing the title "agricultural worker". Whilst all this turmoil was changing the face of the British countryside, the solitary molecatcher was busy about his work. Work that was to become more and more in demand from the very changes that had bought about the decline of others.

The national census that was begun in 1801 and maintained every ten years thereafter provides an indication to the locations of many molecatchers during these difficult times. We can see that they were evenly spread across the country, with pockets of small numbers where the work was plentiful. Their work ranged from the now large farms and estates that had grown from the changes in agriculture, to the request to remove moles from parish land such as churchyards, gardens of the rich and water barriers like those found in the Fenland areas.

A modern steel mole trap set in a mole run

So just how prosperous were molecatchers? The Victorian wage recorded during the 1800s fails to document those of molecatchers, probably because it was as closely a guarded secret as the work itself. We can, however, find evidence from private bill heads and parish records of the sums of money that were changing hands. The Parish molecatcher was employed on an agreed contract for a specified period of time, anything up to 21 years. For this he would have been paid an annual sum, £10, and most molecatchers would work three or four neighbouring parishes. This work was augmented by farms and estates that would pay on average a further 10 shillings for their control, other individuals with land and, of course, the sale of the skins filled the molecatchers' pockets. At a time when the annual recorded wages for agricultural labourers was £30, teachers £40 and government low wage workers £46, the molecatchers were obviously in a very profitable business.

The traveling molecatchers were given board and lodgings and paid for their services; they had regular farms that they would visit, stay a few weeks then move on to the next. Farmers now with a large acreage to tend and sizable flocks to feed required the moles to be removed, as their molehills contaminated fodder crops and rendered land unusable. It has been recorded that many agricultural workers supplemented their income by catching moles in any spare time that they could find, and the poachers also were quick to steal moles from any traps they stumbled upon. The real skill was in the hands of the molecatchers – these extraordinary individuals who were as secretive as the creature they sought, and just as wily.

We know molecatchers peppered the whole of the country so it is another mystery as to how they came to obtain this knowledge. They learnt how moles lived, their habits, how they breed, and of how to make devices to catch them. It is strange also that these devices or traps are of the same design and constructed in the same way. This was obviously a knowledge that has been around for along time – long enough for it to cross the country from coast to coast, through shire to shire – and to reach the remotest of settlements and localities

Superstitions attached to the mole

It may never be known, but perhaps molecatchers themselves were responsible for some of the strange superstitions attached to mole.

Moles have been connected with superstition for centuries. The fact that little was known about the mole probably enhanced the myths that are still around today.

The arrival of molehills around a house was said to foretell a death in the household (so molecatchers would have been in demand when moles were in the neighbourhood). The wearing of a dead mole around the neck was said to cure toothache, and a pair of the mole's large front feet worn as a necklace was said to bring good luck – items that were only available from the gifted few.

Decline of the traditional molecatcher

In an environment where you always work alone, where you may see very few people during the course of a day's work, the skill of the molecatcher was destined to dwindle. A father would perhaps share his knowledge with his son, not to keep a skill alive, but to ensure an income for the family. To share hard-earned knowledge with others could lead to a dividing in the work available, and ultimately to the family's income.

Molecatchers became the victims of their own greed. Their refusal to share specialist knowledge was eclipsed by the introduction of other methods of mole control – poison.

A man with poisons could claim to clear acres of fields in half the time and at half the cost of the traditional molecatcher. The fact that the poisons were untested for this use, and that secondary poisoning of other species would inevitably take place, seemed of little worry to landowners. Strychnine, despite its indiscriminate risk of poisoning, provided a cheaper control that required none of the knowledge or respect of the molecatcher. A new breed of eradicator was born the "Mole Killer". No proof to the works completed could be shown, no wisdom of the mole was important, only a jar of worms soaked in the deadly substance dropped into the moles' tunnels until the digging stopped. The mole killers could take life at a lower cost to that of the molecatchers. In the new economic world of agriculture where the farmers were growing fat, the opportunity for any saving to increase profits was seized.

Not all landowners were quick to change, and some held on to the skill of the molecatchers. Where savings had to be made, like parish accounts, the molecatchers were sometimes dismissed, despite being under an agreed term of employment. It was the demand for mole skin – a commodity that mole killers could not supply – that enabled many of the molecatchers to remain in business. Many had to reduce their costs of catching moles, but this was supported by the increase in price they could ask for mole skins.

The location a molecatcher worked was to become vital to whether they were to survive. Those that worked areas close to major towns almost certainly had an outlet for their moleskins, but towns also provided a retail source for strychnine. Molecatchers working the parishes surrounding the towns often had confrontations with new mole killers spreading out from the streets of fortune. Molecatchers in the remote areas did not escape the competition from poison. The industrial expansion soon reached these areas to also change how they worked; they had to decide whether it was necessary to change codes and become a mole killer or struggle to survive.

The rural economics were changing, as were agricultural ways – machines took over, and slowly like many country crafts and skills, molecatching became a thing of the past. Only pockets of tradition remained – it is these pockets of tradition that allow many of the old ways to continue.

However, I am hopeful for the future of this craft. I believe mole-catching will continue, because we are beginning to realize that the old ways were sometimes the best. The use of the poison has been questioned – it is no longer accepted to administer unnecessary suffering to moles, nor is it permitted to place non-approved substances into the moles' environment (currently there are no substances approved for mole control).

Naturally there are other alternatives, the world of electronics soon realized the possibility to make money from moles, and introduced an electronic device that, when placed in the ground, will keep the garden mole free. But how many of these are needed on farms, sports fields, road verges, estates, public areas and horse paddocks? Who will maintain them, keep the batteries fresh and, more importantly, prevent them from being stolen. Again, the costs of these deterrents runs high compared with the neat metal mole traps available today. The real question is, do they work? A topic for discussion later.

So how will molecatchers' numbers increase again if the knowledge is lost? The need for the number of molecatchers to increase will come from the economics and attitude of our modern world. The countryside is constantly being developed as our need for that modern cottage in a village location (but close to all amenities) grows. Many of these homes are crammed into small spaces that were once fields, fields where moles may have existed for centuries. The only difference now is that now moles have new lodgings with lawn care, grass that is groomed once a week and fed. The vast majority of these home owners will have had little contact with the countryside, and have never seen a mole before. At the first sign of a molehill they will quickly run to the nearest garden center for all sorts of wonderful advice.

MOLE FACT FILE
Male moles are bucks. Female moles are does.

Following a few weeks of trying desperately to plead with the mole to go next door, using a number of options that reach deep into the pocket, they will eventually seek a guaranteed method of permanent removal – the molecatcher. Although trapping is the most humane method of getting rid of a mole, it will be the low cost and permanent solution that will appeal most. The molecatcher's rapid results can only promote the craft, and the arrival of another mole at any time in the future will bring a repeat demand for their services. I believe the numbers of molecatchers can only increase because of this demand, a demand caused by humans intruding into land frequented by the mole.

So how do you become a molecatcher?

Becoming a molecatcher is not easy, and not something that you can achieve from books alone. The knowledge I can pass on in these pages will only be the start of your knowledge. You must learn of the weather, of soil and of how a range of things influences the mole. Ultimately, it is only practical experience that will teach you all you need to know, but in this book I will lay out the foundations.

One gift that molecatching has given to me over the years is an awareness of some of nature's wonders – for being a molecatcher is solitary work, and you will spend a lot of time alone and outside.

Many books have been written on moles, many by people with a greater scholarly knowledge of the complex subject matter of the mole than myself. Indeed, many of these works adjudge the work of the molecatcher as non-essential. I will not shoulder any more of your time on that subject. My humble learning has been jotted down on scraps of paper and logged for my needs in catching moles. Yet it has served me well, and is based not only on theory, but on practice and experience.

2

The mole

We know that the mole was around during the Roman Empire, but mole goes back further than that. Mammals became a vast species about 65 million years ago, and fossils of moles and other underground living creatures have been found on many occasions.

Many species of mole are found worldwide, ranging across the globe from North America to Asia. Our mole here in Europe, *Talpidae Europaea* or the Common Mole, is regarded as a true mole.

The first thing many have to come to terms with is its size – it is far smaller than most people think. All molehills are the work of a tiny creature that can sit in the palm of your hand. The mole weighs in at a quarter of a pound [110–120 grams], and rarely exceeds six inches [150mm] in length. The mole is not blind as many people believe, but has two pin sized eyes. It has very little use for these, however, as it lives in an almost permanently dark world. In fact, where the moles live (and how) is one of the most important things to consider when molecatching.

The fact that moles have poor eyesight tells us that they rely on other senses – to 'feel' the environment in which they live. A mole can hear, but does not require the sensitive hearing of, say, a mouse. The sounds in mole's world are carried through the tunnels (like the speaking tubes once found on ships and in stately homes). This amplifies the sounds, informing the mole of its surroundings.

Moles do make sounds. One sound, a twittering, is said to be communication to others. I have never heard this, but one sound I have heard is the haunting, high-pitched scream mole emits when frightened. Once heard it is never forgotten. Yet if sight and sound are not that important to the life of a mole, how does it sense the environment in which it lives?

Touch. The mole has a covering of sensitive hairs on its face called *Vibrissae*, the bases of which lead to a very perceptive system of nerve endings. In addition, mole runs with its tail in the air, touching the roof of the tunnels like a dodgem car at a fun fair. Held in this position, the tail feels the vibrations from above, warning of the approach of predators above ground. This contact aids with tunnel location for the mole, and for the molecatcher it has an important role in catching the mole (discussed later).

Another, even more sensitive nervous system is connected to thousands of tiny papillae, which cover the mole's nose; these are known as the *Emiers organs*, and it can be filled with blood to increase the level of sensitivity.

The Emiers organs and Vibrissae detect air pressure and air currents, but how does the mole find its way around such a complex world in the dark? Moles have a kinesthetic sense, an imprinted pattern of memory, meaning that it can remember every turn and junction of every tunnel. This highly improved memory sense is similar to that which enables us to find the light switch in a darkened room.

So to recap, we know that mole has poor sight, fair hearing but an excellent memory for direction in an environment that it feels through an acute nervous system. The mole in its dark world has no reason to know whether it is day or night. Nowadays, it probably works this out by the lack of noise above ground during the human's hours of sleep.

How do moles live?

The mole lives a solitary life of between three to five years in a territory it will defend with its life, even against another of the same species. Yes, moles will fight each other.

Mole activity depends upon many factors, covered later on, but the spring mating is probably the most important reason for movement for the mole. This is the only time at which two moles may find it tolerable to be together, and of course it helps with the survival of the species! At this time, the moles actually undergo a change in their bodies. At the end of February, beginning of March, the male's testes increase in size, giving them the urge to seek a mate. The males will travel considerable distances to find a mate, and so as not to be met by aggression from a female, also at this time the female's ovaries are increasing in size. She will accept a male mole's advances for a period of about 24 hours. The desire to mate, be it only for a short time, removes the mole's territorial instincts. The male, having found a female, mates and leaves in search of another female.

This method ensures that all serviceable females are pregnant for the spring. Once the sexual urge has gone, the moles return to their original territorial selves.

The mole's gestation period lasts about four weeks, with the new moles born around the months of April and May. The female gives birth in a nest, which is just a grass (or similar) lined tunnel. Many books detail fortresses, a large mound of soil, which contains the nest. These I have only seen in land that has a high water table, and it has obviously been constructed to keep the nest dry. Should you come across one of these, it will probably be on land where the moles are not a problem because the land is unserviceable – land that floods is usually lacking in moles' food, as the water drowns it. Moles are thus seldom a problem here. If you do find a fortress, stand back and admire the work of the little creature that has achieved such a construction.

The newborn moles are pink at birth and weigh only a few grams. Mole litters vary in size from from an average two or three up to seven (a doe will have eight teats, so eight may be possible). The growth rate is rapid, and they will be three to four inches long in a short time. They are blind at first, with the eyes opening at about three weeks, and the velvet coats also covering them by this time.

Moles do vary in colour in certain parts of the country. In Berkshire (where I catch moles) they can be black, the colour we all expect, but in the east of the country they can be grey. Other colours for moles can be albino, cream, golden and rust. Whether this is colour pigments in the soil affecting the mole's coat or inter breeding and movement I am not sure. In addition, you may find an apricot colour on the under side of the mole's belly. This is thought to be caused by staining from the urine that the mole deposits in the tunnels to mark its territory – the belly fur is probably being used as a brush to spread the scent as the mole journeys through its tunnels. I once caught a mole with markings of a badger – black with a white band down its face and a white under body. A pure white mole has often been reported as having been caught, though I have not caught one myself. Young moles are certainly born light in colour, and a young mole may still have certain light markings until they reach maturity, but large adult moles do also vary in colour in this way.

The mother returns to the nest to feed and check the young several times a day. In fact, the female will tend her new offspring until the day instinct takes over and the young moles set out to begin their new lives as solitary creatures, normally at about 5–6 weeks of age.

Our furry friend!

Whether this instinct is self-controlled or the female's protecting touch now lacking I do not know. However, the whole litter departs in search of a new life. Their mother will probably stay.

At this point in their lives, the young moles are under threat from many natural predators. Owl, crow, fox, cat, stoat and weasel will all seize the opportunity for a meal. Moles are aware of this, and in the search for an ideal home a journey just under the surface is made, reducing the chances of attack. When a mole does this I refer to it as *running spooked*, but in other parts of the country it has other names such as jigging, joking or scribbling. It is not only young moles that do this; adult moles will also run spooked should they be disturbed in some

MOLE FACT FILE
Although you may never experience it, the collective noun for a group of moles is a labour, a labour of moles.

way. The males in search of a female at the spring mating season will run spooked to avoid attack. In dry weather, if you find a mole running spooked in areas with no molehills, probe down a little deeper and you will find the tunnels being used, especially on grass areas. I believe that the moles are at depth in the moist soil where the food source is, but they need to ventilate the tunnels or flush the system with new air. The safest way is to dig a shallow complex above, which will allow new air to enter the tunnels. To just open a shaft would enable predators to enter directly into the tunnels being used, so a system of tunnels close to the surface is a good option.

Where does mole live?

The world of the mole is a complex system of runs and tunnels of varying depths. It is important if you are to catch mole that you understand this world. Many a molecatcher will tell of the importance of watching the weather. In fact, mole can tell of the weather before many a forecaster. The mole must find food if it is to survive, and food it finds in its runs and tunnels. When the weather is fine and mild, the moles' food will be found in shallow runs close to the surface. When the weather turns cold, the temperature pushes the moles' food down into warmer soil. Then the mole will be found in the deeper runs, perhaps below the frost line. This becomes obvious when molehills appear above the frozen snow.

Soil is pushed up existing vertical shafts from these deeper runs, which can vary in depth to almost three feet [1 meter]. If you study mole movements in different weather you will build up an understanding of just how a mole is influenced by the demands the weather places on its food. The worm is the mole's main diet, and having a soft body can feel the pressure of weather changes. This is important to the worm as a cold front may mean being frozen in soil from a hard frost. The worm senses this cold front before it happens, and dives into warmer soil. The mole, needing to eat, is forced to follow.

This can be confirmed by closely watching the barometer, and it is possible to predict the weather by this study – if a mole is suddenly found in deeper runs then cold weather is coming. A hot summer pushes the food down into the moist soil. Again, mole will be found in the deeper runs when the sun has caused the surface soil to dry and crack.

The mole's tunnels are its traps, for its food – worms and other soil-dwelling bugs and grubs – fall into these tunnels and, quickly sensed by the mole, are hunted out and devoured. Depending on the fertility of the soils, the mole will construct a network of tunnels to fulfil its needs, which includes the deeper runs for the colder spells. A mass of molehills is a good indication as to what's going on below – a small area of mole activity may show large sized molehills, and this could be for a number of reasons:

- The mole is at depth.
- There is something buried in the ground the mole is having to dig round.
- Someone has disturbed mole, or the soil may not be holding much food.

After awhile you learn to interpret these signs.

Where did the mole you are looking for come from?

Mole does not drop out of the sky; it has arrived from adjoining land. It may even still be living in that adjoining land, but feeding in the neighbouring area.

Ask yourself why has mole come? Look next door. Has someone disturbed it? Is the land flooded? Is it the breeding season? Is it the time of year for the new moles to find a territory of their own? If you can answer these questions then you are on the way to working out the reason for the mole's arrival, the size of the mole, and you can even guess its sex. This knowledge is only the beginning, but you are on the way to considering the problem like a molecatcher.

Factfile

Do moles eat the roots of plants? This is often asked, and the answer lies in the mouth of a mole. Open mole's mouth and there are forty-four teeth, each designed to eat meat. Mole's main diet is worms as well as other bugs and grubs that happen to fall into its runs.

The mole must eat almost its own body weight in food each day. Often a mole will hunt more than its requirements, then bite the heads off worms and leave them to grow another head (when eaten, worms are eagerly consumed head first). As worms cannot move until they have grown another head, and this takes a number of weeks, the mole has provided itself with a larder.

Female moles tend to increase their tunnels and runs prior to and during the mating season, and my experience has led me to believe that this is to increase the number of worms stored in worm larders, so as to provide for the female whilst rearing the new young. Another point to consider when assessing the problem that I will cover under amorous moles later on!

The mole can move at a staggering two miles per hour (4 kilometres per hour) in the tight network of tunnels, and the famous smooth

TOP TIP
When the weather is cold and the ground is hard or it has been very wet, use a probe with a slightly thicker diameter then you would normally use – it will be easier to find the tunnels.

velvet fur (without any lay) means that it can turn in the smallest of spaces. Another point to consider when assessing the problem that will be covered under amorous moles later.

3

Catching your first mole

Most people's first experience of a mole will be following the appearance of a molehill. The arrival of molehills will initially be sudden, as moles must dig to provide that much needed food. The greater the food source available, the less digging is required, so if the ground is lacking in food then the mole must do more digging and a larger tunnel complex will be needed.

People often do not realize that a mole can dig at an astonishing speed. I have sat and watched a mole dig and deposit dirt on the surface at an alarming rate. In thirty minutes enough soil was piled high to fill a two-gallon bucket, and this was in heavy ground. In well-tilled soil you can expect a mole's progress to be quicker.

Many believe the mole has blocks of sleep and work. I agree that they do tend to have periods of rest and work, and study of a particular mole may result in the approximate times of activity. To put actual times to moles, generally say four hours on four hours off, is a little questionable, as no mole lives to an exact timetable. However, it is generally accepted that the males are more active than the females. Certain features would dictate to any mole's periods of activity, human or natural disturbances.

To catch your mole you have to enter into its world, but before you can do this it is important to find the tunnels and runs the mole uses and, even more importantly, you must find the right one. Often the pattern of molehills on the surface has little or no bearing on the network below. You cannot just take a spade and start digging into the mole's world. Instead you must search for the runs in a more subtle way.

The first tool you will need is a probe. I use a steel bar with a wooden handle for comfort. You can use a large screwdriver or something similar. This will be a tool you have to become used to handling, as it is the only contact you have with mole's environment from above ground. To use the probe, simply push it down into the ground where you think a run is. If you are right a sudden 'give' will be felt as the probe breaks into the run. Using a probe reduces the damage to the mole's world, which in turn reduces the chances of your interference being detected. Due to its highly developed senses, the mole is possibly already aware you are around, and it is important to work quickly and with as little disturbance as possible. To damage a mole's run only to discover you're in the wrong place will alert the mole to your intentions.

Finding the right run is not the mystery, as many molecatchers will lead us to believe. To prove this, let's look at a typical mole complex. The mole, having entered into the property from a perimeter, will have tunnels to and from this adjoining area. These tunnels will lead to the feeding area, other tunnels will extend out further, and these will be the tunnels used to increase the feeding areas. The runs to look for are the main runs into the area and the tunnels that extend out. It is in these runs that the mole will be moving to access areas in which to work. In the feeding areas, the mole will be constantly cleaning out fallen soil to ensure a smooth hunting ground. The cleaning and digging involves moving soil, and the chances of a trap being blocked or *bunged*, even sprung with soil, is high, so try not to place traps in these runs.

Remember when probing to consider the time of year. There is no point probing in shallow runs in cold weather. Once you have determined the run you are to use, probe around the site to establish the direction it runs. Ideally, you want a straight run, with no bends – remember, mole has a kinesthetic sense, and any straightening of the run will quickly be detected.

Finding the right run may take time, until you become more experienced. Molecatchers do this every day, often in soils they have worked for years. (I will cover probing and selecting a trap site again later, as many people find this to be the most difficult phase of molecatching.) One mystery of molecatching is how molecatchers always know where the runs are. I suggest that this is probably because they have been catching moles in that particular ground for years! For example, many of the people I catch for are amazed at seeing a single push of the probe produce a straight run and a catch overnight, but this is not so amazing if you have been catching moles there for years and they have only recently moved in.

Modern Traps

Before we enter into mole's world, let's have a look at the traps available today. We have already looked at the traps of old, so let's learn about the new traps.

To catch a mole you will have to decide which trap you are to use. Every molecatcher has a favourite. Many will speak of the benefits of one type over another, and I am no different. I prefer the metal half-barrel. but it's all down to personal preferences.

Let me explain some of the traps and their setting, then you can make your own decision about which to use. I am often asked how many traps does it take to catch a mole... and the answer is simple... .only one.

Let's begin with the *Scissor* or *Pincher* trap, as this is the trap most frequently seen in garden centres and hardware shops. Powered either by a flat spring or a small-coiled spring, these traps are all made from metal. As the name suggests, the traps operate using a scissor action, and the different types of this trap all work in the same way. Depressing the top, which opens the jaws and places the spring under tension, sets them. A retaining plate is located between the jaws, which holds them open.

The trap is sprung when the mole passes between the jaws, pushing the plate and thus freeing the spring to return to its original position. In doing so it catches the mole in the jaws. These traps vary in small details such as jaw shape, but the principles are all the same.

A *loop* trap is also metal in construction. It has a flat top from which two loops are pushed down. A retaining bar holds them down, preventing the spring from returning to its original position. Another bar acts as a release – it is set at an angle, and when mole pushes past, it releases the spring, which pulls the loops up catching the mole. Both the scissor and the loop traps have one thing in common – when they have been sprung, the trap is inoperative because both the jaws and loops are sprung. This makes it impossible to catch two moles in one trap, which means that extra traps may be needed if more than one mole is to be caught.

The *metal half barrel* trap can, and will, catch two moles as it has independent springs. The arched shape of the trap body when set in the mole's runs acts like the roof of the tunnel. Two thin metal bars are shaped into the trap loops and are large enough to allow a mole to pass through. These are connected to the small coiled springs, which in turn are held independently by a spring retaining bar, which is released by another smaller loop – the mumble pin that the mole pushes when releasing the trap. Pressing the top of the large loop down through the

TOP TIP
When asked how many traps it takes to catch a mole,
the reply is... one.

arched roof sets the trap, applying tension to the spring. It is easier to do this by pointing the trap down slightly and then flicking the retaining bar over the top so that it rests on the release catch. A small adjustment to locate it under the release hook at the top of the mumble pin, the same the other end, and the trap is set. This trap sounds worse to set than it actually is – as with most things, practice soon makes perfect.

Recently a new trap has appeared in the UK from Holland. The Talpex Trap is a cross between the scissor and half barrel trap. It is a longer version of the scissor or Pincher trap, employing the use of a larger coil spring. The main selling point of this trap is the power in the coil spring – at seven kilograms it certainly operates with a force. This force must be overcome when setting it, which is achieved by squeezing the top like the scissor trap. Those with a weak grip may struggle. The Talpex trap is sensitive in operation, but like so many other traps, it has limitations. It requires more tunnel disturbance to place in the runs than a half barrel traps as it is slightly wider. Is it a good trap? Only time will tell.

When you decide to purchase any traps, set them first to ensure that it is a trap that you want and can use. Ask for assistance from the shop assistant, and try all that are available... but be warned! Remember to keep your fingers clear. I cannot think of anything more embarrassing than catching a finger in a trap while in a shop. Perhaps asking the shop assistant to show you how to set it would be best.

The benefits of each trap

The metal half-barrel trap can be set at any depth with no more soil disturbance than when it is set in a shallow run, and it is completely out of sight when in use, unlike the scissor traps. The arched top forms a nice roof to the mole's runs – the flat topped loop trap does not (remember, moles run with their tail in the air feeling the roof). An arched top, if set correctly, will not alarm the mole before the trap is sprung.

All of these different traps have advantages over one another. The scissor or pincher trap can be viewed without disturbing the trap site, because the long arms stand out and, if spread wide, it indicates that the trap has been sprung. The half-barrel trap has to be uncovered when checking it, as it is completely out of sight. The fact that the half-barrel trap is out of sight may be advantageous, especially if setting it in areas of human disturbance.

Caring for your traps

Having obtained your traps, there are a few key points to remember. They will not work unless properly cared for – you cannot expect a trap to sit on a shelf in a shed for six months and still hope for it to produce results.

I keep my traps in a rubber-lined canvas bag. In there they are safe from contamination. I have often seen mole traps neatly in place on a shelf, but next to the pesticides and fertilisers. You can catch moles with new or contaminated traps, but why risk a miss due to strange smells pervading into the mole's environment? I keep everything I use for molecatching in the one bag, and any dirt collected on the traps or other items used also goes into the bag. This way everything is housed in dirt. Sometimes I have placed a dead mole in the bag to increase the scent.

Having obtained your traps I suggest you bury them in some dirt to tarnish them. I have read that molecatchers once boiled their traps in water with wild nuts to take all the smells away – if we recall the strong senses that moles possess, it does seem sensible to condition our new traps somehow.

Before you use your traps, here are some tips to help give you the edge over the mole.

Scissor or pincher traps

Never oil the flat springs when they show signs of rust, stiff brush them with a wire brush instead. The centre plate often requires a fair push by the mole to release it, especially when a new trap with good springs is used. Detach the plate and place it in a vice. With a small flat file, change the angle slightly so that the plate can be pushed with less force. This technique cannot be applied to the scissor traps, which have a round bar for the plates to rest upon.

The Half Barrel trap

The arched barrel shape of the trap body in most new traps is a little too flat for me, but they can be squeezed to the size required. Remember to adjust the large trap loops so they pass freely through the slots in the arched plate when operated.

The mumble pins or small loops with which mole releases the traps are often a little large, and smaller moles sometimes get part of their body through. Again, a gentle squeeze will reduce them in diameter.

The release hooks are often too curved on half barrel traps, requiring quite a force to release them. They can be reduced with a pair of pliers, though. It is important to always inspect all your traps for weak springs. Traps in use keep the springs under constant tension in all weather conditions, and they will eventually become weak. These should be discarded immediately, as weak springs will not catch cleanly or humanely.

As a general rule, a trap can be re-used about twenty times before it needs to be replaced.

TOP TIP *PRACTICE*
Find some locations that have mole activity and probe around, walk gently around and practice locating the runs and tunnels. You will soon learn the layout of that territory.

So what else do you need to catch a mole?

You have the probe, traps and something to keep them in. So what else will you need? Obviously, you will have to enter into the mole's runs and tunnels to place the trap, and the best tool for this is a small trowel. This need not be gold, sliver or chrome plated – though a cheap one should be avoided if you are to put it to plenty of use. I use a normal garden trowel, and always carry a spare. I also carry a rough sharpening stone to keep the edge on the trowel sharp. I feel this is important as a sharp trowel cuts cleanly and positively into the ground, especially when cutting through turf. It does not damage the tunnel too much and should you need to shape or clean any tunnels, this can be carried out cleanly in the same way that a sharp chisel cuts and shapes wood. A knife is always handy, and I am a firm believer in big is best in this field. A six-inch [150mm]-plus blade and sharpener is used for a wide range of tasks, but mainly cutting through roots that mole often chooses to dig under. It must be stressed that a knife should have a good stout handle, as much of the time it will be used with wet, muddy or cold hands. Sew the sheath to the outside of the bag to avoid scrabbling for your knife and this will reduce the risk of an accident.

It is often a good idea to carry a pair of pliers with you for making any alterations to the traps, and I always carry spare spring retaining bars for the half-barrel trap.

I have a tool I made up to press and smooth the base of a run when I have opened it up. When a mole passes along a run it polishes the

TOP TIP
If you have trouble catching with these traps, try leaving a mound in the centre of the run and place the trap directly over it. The mole with be encouraged slightly up as it runs along and will release the trap more effectively.

TOP TIP
For the Arouse trap, tie a small piece of string to the wire square to avoid it being lost following the mole springing the trap.

tunnel with its underside; pressing down the base and smoothing it leaves it as the mole expects to find it. To do this I have a piece of wood 2 inches [50mm] in diameter mounted on a handle. It is also useful to collect a quiver of hazel sticks, which again can be attached to the bag. In areas where there is little human disturbance they are ideal to mark trap sites.

Most of today's molecatchers need to travel, not sadly as the old molecatchers on foot or by cart, but by motor vehicle, so a towel to wipe your hands clean with is another necessary item.

One tool that is not so easy to carry in the bag but which is often quite useful is a rake to smooth out the molehills. It is advisable to do this if you are starting work on a large area like a field when the weather has been unkind. A few days of constant wet weather is not unknown in England, and it soon hides the working area. Raking them out under these conditions allows the mole's territory to be understood, as mole works new soil to the surface. The raking of a finished job is normally left for the client, as they may wish to leave the hills or gather up the soil, so check first. (Personally, I use mole dirt for my indoor plants and containers – I mix it in with a good one-part potting compost to two-parts dirt, and I find that it works very well.)

If you are catching moles in public areas, a ball of coloured string is handy for marking trap sites (this is explained in more detail later on).

For those who seek to know more, then quote my molecatcher's formula:

A trap in the correct run will do its job,
The amount of correct runs depends on the number of moles present,
Which depends on the season,
Which will dictate the weather
Which will dictate to the worms,
Who will dictate to the mole,
Which will determine how many runs the mole will make,
Which will determine how many correct runs there will be,
Which will determine how many traps will be used.
It's simple

Still not sure on finding the right run?

This is a problem most people have. To try and clarify this, the diagram on page 37 should make it clear. The mole will have entered from a perimeter – it may be living in adjoining land or on a boundary line, but it will enter down runs to the feeding ground. These runs are found in what I indicate as the *hatched zone*, and they take the mole direct to the feeding grounds, which I have indicated as the *dotted zone*. Moles will extend this dotted zone (or their feeding ground) to meet their require-ments, and these runs will be extended out to do this (I refer to this area as the *shaded zone*). When probing, look at the mole territory carefully and ascertain where the mole has come from, and probe to find the hatched zone runs. Here is the first place to site your traps, as moles will be travelling at speed to feed and a clean catch is possible. The next best site for your traps is in the shaded zone, where the mole will again be travelling to the extent of the tunnels to increase the dotted zone. In the diagram, the run in the shaded zone has a junction, so set the trap prior to this for a better chance of a catch. Remember to try and place the trap in areas where the mole will not be working the soil – it is possible to catch in the dotted zone, but mole will be constantly clearing soil from the hunt-ing area. In this area, mole will possibly bung or spring the trap with soil.

The use of the probe must become second nature. To walk around

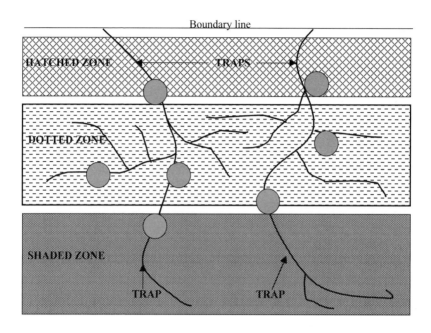

just pushing it in and out of the ground only frustrates, and does unnecessary damage to the mole's environment, which only results in the mole causing more damage by further digging. When you have decided where the zones are, make an educated guess to the probable location of a run.

Then probe down slowly. If no run is found within a few probes, start again. Consider the water table, what has the weather been doing over the past few days? Remember that some runs bear no relation to the location of molehills.

The placing of traps in the ground

When you have decided that the run you have found is the one you are to place the trap in, it is important that you have everything ready. I normally take less than a minute to set a trap, and speed is very important. The reason will become clear as I explain the procedure. The principles for all types of trap are much the same, but let's take one at a time.

It is a good practice to grab a handful of dirt from a molehill and rub your hands with it just to reduce any unwanted smells that may be on your skin. I have heard of people who work in gloves, but this can make setting the traps quickly and correctly more difficult.

Placing and setting the Scissor and Pincher traps

Having probed down, take a trowel and cut a neat square into the run, try not to push through the run to its base, only cut into the roof. Remove the turf and any loose dirt that may have fallen in. Look into the run and check to see if the sides and base are smooth. This is a sure sign that the run is indeed in use, as the mole's fur polishes it as it passes through. Should you see any vegetation growing in the run, then forget it, because this means that it is unused. Vegetation growing through a molehill is a sure sign of an unused mole run.

The hole the trowel digs will be the right size for these traps. Firm down the sides and base, and with the trap already set, push it down into the run. Ensure that the shape of the jaws lines up nicely with the shape of the run. The aim of good trap setting is to place a trap and leave the site as the mole expects to find it. I will describe the replacement of the roof later.

The Loop trap

The procedure here is almost the same, as the hole size this trap requires is only slightly larger than that of the scissor trap. When placing the trap in the hole, having first firmed the sides and base, ensure that the top of the trap is lined up with the top of the mole run. Ensure also that there is enough clearance for the loops to rise up. The large flat plate of this trap does not sit comfortablly in the run. I have caught moles with it and I found it catches better in the shallow runs.

The Half-barrel trap

When using this trap and having decided which run to place it in, probe down on either side of the first probe hole to ensure that the tunnel is straight and long enough for the larger size of this trap

As with all the traps, have it set and ready. The reason for having the traps set is that the moles will feel airflows and pressure changes. To delay the operation any longer than is necessary will possibly alert the mole to your presence. Air entering from above tells the mole that a tampering of the runs by an external force has occurred. Only two things would enter into mole's environment – one is a weasel (as they are small enough to squeeze in the tunnels), and the other is a mole-catcher.

Molecatchers often wear hats, which they place over the hole should a delay occur, this also prevents the rain entering when catching in the wet. A wet patch would be another sign that the roof had been tampered with.

Next with the trowel cut a hole in the same way as for the other traps. Then with the hand feel in the hole to confirm the direction of the tunnels, and check for any bends. Until you get used to the setting of this trap, place it on the surface and cut around it with the trowel. The hole must be a tight fit for the trap. Clean out any loose dirt and firm the base and sides.

Push the trap into the run, making sure that the arched top of the trap lines up perfectly with the roof of the run. The large trap loops can be pushed down gently into the base to achieve this.

Push gently to avoid springing the trap. There are no repeatable words for the sudden rapping of cold knuckles when a trap does this on frosty mornings. It must be stressed that a snug fit is essential. There must be enough room for the springs to operate above the trap.

A new trap is currently appearing on the shelves of garden centres, based on the *Arouze* trap. The *Arouze* trap originates in France, and no mole reference would be complete with a mention of it. I have used such a trap, and admit that little soil disturbance is needed. They are used in the same way as for a scissor trap, but I feel their best use is in well-tilled soil when mole is running spooked. The construction from a single piece of thick sprung wire held apart by a small wire square enables them to be simply pushed into the soil and left. Any mole moving in this loose soil is caught when it pushes through dislodging the wire square and causing the trap to close.

This new trap does require a fair amount to force to set, and if the hands are weak or arthritic then I feel they would be hard to operate. Their use in cold wet weather could cause much frustration, as the wires, being round, tend to slip as you balance one on the other. Initially, I found that the mole pushed this trap over rather than pushed into it, but with practice it can be put to use. The gap for the mole to pass trough could be wider once the trap is set, but these are small points, and as with all things, you pay your money and take your choice.

The Talpex Trap

The Talpex trap is placed in the same way as the half barrel trap due to its length although it operates like the scissor or pincher trap. When in its set position it is wider than the half barrel trap and this requires the trapper to widen the tunnel in the trap site slightly in hard soil, but in soft soil it can be pushed down allowing the jaws to cut into the side of the tunnel. Ensure the base of the trap site is flat and smooth as any soil left in the tunnel can release the sensitive mumble pin when pushing the trap into place.

Covering the trap

There now comes a difference of opinion regarding covering the trap. I have heard it said that leaving a small hole in the roof of the trap site encourages the mole to the area to check out the problem. In my opinion, the mole would certainly come to the trap site, but only to seal off the run. Leaving an opening may convince the mole that a weasel has entered, and it will choose to block off the tunnel rather than use it again. In doing so, it may spring the trap with dirt.

So I strongly recommend that the trap site covering is tight and secure. This leaves the site as the mole expects to find it. The turf that is

Setting a trap

removed when first you cut into the runs is used. Often it is better if you knock the dirt off it with the trowel. This lightens the weight and makes it easy to mould it for a better fit. With a scissor trap, break the turf into pieces that fit all the gaps the trap leaves around the hole. Three is normal, which includes a small piece for the middle. Loose dirt is sprinkled around the site, and to be one hundred percent sure of keeping all the light and moisture out, place a flowerpot over the top. Many people try and cover trap sites in a very particular fashion, with every little bit of dirt in the right place – it's not necessary.

The half-barrel trap, when covered properly, is completely unnoticeable. However, if the depth of the run is shallow, and to allow the springs to rise fully, would mean the springs rising above the ground level, make a molehill from the cut turf and soil and cover with loose dirt. This then blends in as a molehill. If hiding the trap is not so important, it can be covered with loose dirt only – again, the power of the spring will overcome this. A covering of loose dirt may not keep all the moisture out, but in a shallow run a certain amount of water will penetrate anyway, so do not worry too much about this.

The loose dirt covering will suffice for the loop trap due to the plate top, but if at depth, cover as for the half-barrel trap. If catching in private areas, it is possible to mark your traps with a stick or other prominent mark, but in public areas the traps will need marking secretly if you cannot remember exactly where the sites are. This is where that ball of coloured string comes in that I mentioned earlier. Tie a piece of coloured string to the trap that's long enough to break the surface and be visible. I find most people will think nothing of a piece of string on

TOP TIP
If you find a half barrel trap has been sprung but no mole or soil in the trap reset it and turn it around in the run, if you come back and the same spring has released check the tuning as the spring maybe over powering the catch.

TOP TIP
Buy a nailbrush and nail clippers. You will need them as dirt under the nails is a common discomfort and comes with the job.

the ground, and definitely not enough to stop to pick it up. The secret marking of traps is necessary, as many people will quite happily remove a trap they encounter even if they have no need for it, or they don't know how to use it. If setting traps where machinery is to be used, mark the trap site with a white topped stick so the drivers can see them, a stick is good if snow is expected.

The Talpex trap can be covered in the same way as either the scissor or half barrel, depending on the tunnel it has been set in. The power of the coil spring will overcome quite a lot of resistance, so it is possible to pack cut turf around the trap if it protrudes above the ground.

Checking the traps

Having spent time and care with the traps and also puzzled over where to put them, the next task is probably the hardest. Leave them alone. It will do no good at all keep running to a trap site and disturbing it in eager anticipation of catching that mole. Your movements would be detected by the mole and act as a possible warning. Remember that modern traps catch by design. This makes it possible to leave the traps, but they *must* be checked within twenty-four hours. When checking a trap, do not just run in and pull it from the ground. Look around – has there been any more mole activity? New digging does not mean the trap has not caught, but should it have not caught or been dug through you have already built up a picture of what may be happening. Patience is something a molecatcher must have.

The excitement of pulling a trap from the ground to find it empty will make any trapper disgruntled. The molecatcher seeks an explanation, and it is best to have the answers before the questions. If the trap did not catch, ask yourself why. Did light or moisture enter the run? Did you straighten that slight bend? Has any disturbance from another party intervened during your absence? Whatever the reason, you find you cannot blame the traps for your mistakes. I hope you understand why it is important to work out these possibilities before the trap is inspected. Once I stood disappointed having pulled a soil-filled trap from the ground. After puzzling out the problem, and possible reasons for this failure, I found I had allowed constant rushes of air to enter the tunnels. This ensured that the mole was obviously already aware of the trap site without announcing the fact. I have never done it again since.

There is no demand these days to sport a real moleskin waistcoat, and plumbers no longer use the smooth velvet to craft a pipe joint, so having caught the mole it can be disposed of.

Disposing of a mole not killed cleanly by the traps

If you maintain and monitor your traps properly, you may never have to carry out the worst job of all of molecatching – the dispatching of a live mole in a trap. However, there will be times when a trap has not been set correct or the mole has pushed enough soil into the trap to hinder its operation and the mole is held up against the roof of a trap cushioned by the soil. This will happen in wet soils when the pressure on the mud from the mole's pushing moulds into the trap. The mole entering the trap and springing it then results in the mole only being held. When inspecting a trap site, always consider this possibility, and be prepared to act quickly and positively without a second thought. Any hesitation will cause unnecessary suffering to the mole. Never check a trap without having something to hand with which to dispatch a live mole in the trap. A priest, a purpose made instrument used to dispatch animals and game, is ideal, but for speed you can use your trowel.

A quick sharp blow to the back of the head with the back of the trowel will kill the mole instantly. Whichever trap you use, there is a chance of this happening. If you are using a scissor or talpex trap, lift it from the ground by the top, turn the trap so the mole is facing away from you, and dispatch it quickly. The half-barrel trap is basically the same; lift the trap from the ground by the raised spring and turn the trap so that the mole is facing away, and dispatch it. The trowel is used because it will always be to hand – the wide metal blade of the trowel means a sure, quick and weighted contact that will carry out the task effectively. The mole will bleed through the ears instantly.

Never try to remove a live mole from the trap – the trap holding the mole makes the task easier. Killing a mole is not a pleasant job, and the sight of a live mole in a trap is not pleasing either. I must stress that the sight of the mole alive in the trap must not influence your quick end to the mole. To try and release the mole back into the ground could administer suffering and prolonged death by possible injury received in the initial capture. Although the mole may look unharmed, there may be internal injuries.

It is important that traps are checked regular to reduce any suffering
.

Why not catch mole alive and let him go?

A week never goes by with out some remark made about catching the mole alive and releasing it elsewhere. This is all very well, but where do you let a mole go? It may well sound the kind thing to do, but is it?

Consider what you know about the mole now. The first thing is that a mole cannot be released into an area where moles are present. Remember, to place two moles together out of the breeding season results in a battle of such ferocity that one mole may die as a result, and any survivor will have been subjected to unnecessary distress.

The abandonment of Animals act 1960 section 1 makes it an offense to release an animal into an environment if it does not have a reasonable chance of survival.

The modern world is producing traps of all sizes and shapes to catch live animals, and mole is no exception. Mole traps are now available that catch mole alive. They may well keep animal rights activists happy, but spare a thought for the mole. The design of a trap that encases an animal in its own environment, not allowing its escape, has to cause prolonged unnecessary suffering. I have seen these traps left in people's lawns after I have been called in following their failure to catch the mole. A common problem in the use of these humane traps is the intention to inspect the trap site when the trap is in operation often is over come by other domestic issues. Most traps are purchased during the weekend visit to the garden centre. The trap is placed in the ground, and whilst the intention to check it exists, the weekend passes and it is suddenly Monday and everyone is busy again. Before long, a 24-hour period has passed and any trapped mole is still stuck in this 'humane' trap. As the trap uses no spring, no law has been broken, yet without food the mole will probably be dead or close to death. The result of this trap is that the mole has been subjected to the most inhumane experience.

The suffering these live traps causes needs addressing, and only those in higher places can decide what future there is for such devices. The Department of the Environment, Food and Rural Affairs [DERFA] has recently accepted the need to print a statement that they do not recommend the relocation of moles due to the territorial nature of the animal. As it is also an offense to relocate a pest onto another person's land without permission, and in complying with The Abandonment of Animals Act 1960, I see no reason at all for these devices to be available at all.

A well-kept secret

Many molecatchers often place a dead mole in the run to encourage other moles to the trap site. This takes advantage of the mole's wish to live a solitary life, and the dead mole compels them to seek it out and remove it from their territory. Sometimes dead moles left in territories may encourage others into an area. This would keep the molecatcher in demand. It must be pointed out that to remove a mole from an area may not mean the removal of all moles, and should a mole be nearby it may well move into the now empty, pre-dug territory. If this should happen, do not worry as by then you would have caught your first mole, and to catch another will start to become second nature.

4

Catching moles in different seasons and weathers

Catching in the snow

There will come a time when you may have to catch a mole in the winter when the ground is covered with nature's blanket. Many other animals will hibernate at this time, but the mole will still be busy going about its daily life at a depth dictated by the food source. The food will be at a depth determined by the cold weather. Catching under these conditions is a little different to normal catching, but you must allow for the depth the runs will be at, so there is no point having a probe that won't reach.

When you have found the run, clear away the snow by gently scraping with the side of the trowel. Ensure no snow enters the run when you have opened it up, and work quickly to avoid that cold air entering into the runs and warning the mole. Cover the traps as normal – don't try and pack snow over the trap site to hide it, as any further snowfalls will hide your work quicker, and a thaw would expose the trap site anyway. Mark the trap site with a suitable item (a hazel stick is ideal).

Many people have trouble catching when colder weather strikes. Molehills seem to appear before your very eyes. The pattern becomes an absolute nightmare, and as for finding the zones, well, you would have more chance of finding gold at the end of a rainbow. The secret here is to make the mole tell you where the runs are... well, the runs that mole is using. The ground will obviously be quite hard when the frost touches it, so you need to trample the territory before the frost arrives when the ground is soft. In the morning when you look, mole will have opened out the run used to get to the feeding ground. You may then probe to find the run being used. Better still, wait until later in the new day and the mole will clean out more runs to feed. The new molehills can then be probed to find the run linking the first two new molehills. The trap should be placed here. It must be carried out in this order, and cannot be carried out under normal conditions, because to disturb a mole like this under normal conditions will only cause further damage in other areas. Remember, in cold conditions moles will be demanding more food to survive.

In the colder months this food will not be multiplying, and therefore the mole will need to increase the feeding areas, so larger molehills and areas of damage will be experienced as the mole fulfills its demand for food. The important factor when catching in the colder months is the movement of the sun on the area the mole is damaging. The sun's rays will provide an area of warm soil which normally will be a better location that the moles food will be found. Obviously the mole will choose this area to seek its food. Watching the path the sun takes over the location and the time of day its journey is made will provide vital information on when and where to place traps.

Catching in hot weather

The hot weather in the summer often leads people to believe that the mole has disappeared, but as in the cold weather, moles will be at depth below the hard dry soil where it is still moist.

Should the need arise to catch a mole under these conditions (which is rare due to the lack of actual indication of mole activity), you will need to probe deep. This is difficult in the hard ground, so a stout probe is required. Should you feel you know where the run is, dig down with a trowel to find it. It is important to note that moles will also be using old tunnels rather than digging in the hard soil.

Once you have found a run, the trap must be fitted tightly. Ideally, it is a slow job to get the right fit, but this job must always be carried out at speed. Covering the trap is important, as the shaft dug in hard soil tends to allow access to all manner of things, and is difficult to seal because the soil removed is also hard and dry. It may be necessary to cover the trap site with loose dry dirt if you cannot find any turf. It will probably not rain, so a damp patch in the tunnel is not a worry, unless a sprinkler is being used. Loose dry dirt will not impede the operation of a good half-barrel trap.

There is not normally a rush to catch moles in the hot months, although I get a few usually from those who continually use sprinklers, thus encouraging worms into the lawn. Should you be sitting in the garden yourself sipping a cool drink when the telephone rings, tell them to turn the sprinkler down and enjoy the rest of the day.

Today's gardens are equipped with a wide range of gadgets and gizmos of which the most popular are irrigation systems designed to provide a regular watering. These systems obviously do have an impact on the presence of moles. Nowadays, July is as busy a month for catching moles as any other in urban areas.

It's raining again

There will come a time when you will have to catch a mole in the rain or following prolonged wet spells. Should the mole be in the garden, you may wish to wait until the mole settles down and the ground dries out. The molecatcher needs to know what the mole is doing under these wet conditions. Under prolonged rain the saturation of the ground will place extensive pressure on the mole's food source. The

TOP TIP
Moles deposit their waste in the soil waste so do not
be surprised if you find a moles bottom peering at you
from a moving mole hill!

mole will move to dry soil, under trees or amongst heavy foliage, where moisture will be absorbed or sheltered. The mole will not be working tunnels that are flooded, despite being an excellent swimmer, as there will be little food to consume. The food will, like the mole, move to soil that is less saturated. The mole may even retreat to other areas – the excavation of mounds or high banks is a favourite, where moisture naturally drains away. Here the probing for runs will be hampered by the wet and the depth at which the mole may be working.

It is commonly believed that moles along riverbanks drown when rivers flood, but this is not generally true. It is the mole's food source that drowns, and the moles will return to the riverbanks once the worm populations have recovered.

So should prolonged rainfall start to saturate the ground where you are catching, consider the water table and decide whether it would be better to work areas of higher ground. It is not always heavy rainfall that causes a mole to move territory. I have caught moles at many locations where the natural slope of the landscape, in conjunction with normal weather conditions, means the mole has moved up from the lower level to the higher level as the water table has dictated. This would be obvious should you find a landscape that has a natural pond at the lower level. In the summer the mole would be in the wetter soil around the pond, and as the season changes, the mole would move up away from the pond area that will obviously become wetter.

Should you ever have to remove a mole from fields or gardens that are bordered by a thick fence, a post and rail, etc., then probe the areas beneath and just out from the obstruction, as the moisture content here is ideal for the mole. The constant drip from rain and the run off from the fences will mean the soil will normally be wetter than the surrounding ground. This makes tunnelling easy, and once you have found the run a catch will be almost guaranteed. This is a good place to consider placing a trap in the event of reduced rainfall. The naturally damp areas will attract worms and thus moles, and these runs could be productive.

Worm casts are an indication as to the contents of that particular area. In a heavy concentration of worms where the casts are spread all over the ground, it is obvious why the mole has come to this area. Under wet conditions, mole may have spread out from a border or shrubbery onto the lawn area. This will be because the ground in the shrubbery may be waterlogged, and the food has moved to slightly drier areas, normally the lawn. Worm casts would confirm this. This usually happens if the shrubbery or border is south/southwest facing. I must emphasize that it will only be under prolonged wet periods that this may happen; in normal weather conditions an area facing this front would be ideal for worms source and therefore moles.

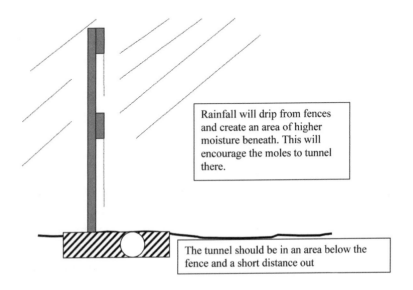

Rainfall will drip from fences and create an area of higher moisture beneath. This will encourage the moles to tunnel there.

The tunnel should be in an area below the fence and a short distance out

Worms

Molecatchers need to know the ecology of worms as it is their presence that influences the presence of moles. There are many different species of worm, but the earthworm is the favoured food of the mole. Earthworms are megadriles; they are hermaphrodites (both male and female), and are of great value to both gardeners and farmers alike. Preferring a soil PH of 7.00, they move through the soil by the movement of tiny bristles (setae) and the secretion of lubricating mucus. As it moves it ingests organic materials in the soil, which is ground up, digested and deposited behind it.

Worm behaviour is dictated by the weather. After heavy rain they will be found near or on the surface, as water-logged soil has insufficient oxygen. It is obvious to a molecatcher that the mole understands this, and the moles' tunnels – which contain areas of space – will provide a supply of oxygen where worms can survive until mole comes along. Some worms come to the surface to mate, and moving over a wet surface enables them to move faster and colonise new areas more quickly. However, when on the surface they can die quickly when exposed to direct sunlight with its strong UV content.

We know how dependent moles are on food, and the importance of the content of food available in an area of land. Basically, like the weather, the population of worms influences the mole population, so a rule of thumb for a molecatcher is – in oak woodland 100 worms per square meter can be found, and in orchard grass 500 worms per square meter can be found. That is why moles can always be found in orchards.

TOP TIP
In some cases the ground is hard and the mole has been running spooked (running shallow) don't be fooled by this. Often there is a small spoil, just a little mound. Carefully open this up and slowly dig down. There will be a tunnel at depth below it. Trust me.

5

Molecatching tips and hints

Folklore has it that to be a real molecatcher you have to be bitten by a mole first. This is because to be quiet enough and to have enough opportunity to be bitten means that you must have a lot of contact with moles.

Over the years you will build up little tricks of the trade. I feel these little tips must be written down so that hopefully it will encourage others to do the same, and by doing so we can ensure that the art of molecatching does not fade away again. I have included some of my tips and tricks in this section.

The ten-minute mole

In the late summer and autumn months when the young moles are seeking new territories, it is sometimes possible to catch the 'ten-minute mole'. This mole is often caught well within ten minutes and is always a new mole working a fresh area.

This can only be carried out if fresh workings are being dug and the molehills are moving when you arrive. Sometimes the sight of birds, particularly starlings, massing amongst molehills is a sure sign that a mole is active below, as worms sense the threat and rise up away from the mole. Study the ground and work out where the mole has come from – you are looking for the hatched zone (shown in the diagram on page 32). Move slowly and carefully around the area to this point and probe to find a run. This movement must be slow and quiet. Only move when the mole is pushing soil up and the spoil heap is moving. Quickly set the trap in the run and cover tightly to make sure no light is entering.

Move slowly back so the mole is between you and the hatched zone. Again, when the mole is pushing soil, push the probe in the ground – it is not important to find a run. Then with the trowel tap the probe two or three times. Pull the probe out move sideways one pace and repeat. Do this across the area then forward one pace and across again. Repeat until you have walked a pattern across and to the trap site.

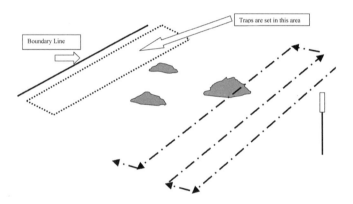

Check the trap for the mole, which should be caught. This technique cannot be carried out with an old mole; it will only work on a new season one. I have often caught the ten-minute mole, and people do not

TOP TIP
It must be considered that the mole has left the area before your arrival if there is little mole activity in the surrounding areas to the location and your traps have failed to catch in 24–48 hours.

TOP TIP
When a mole is running spooked and you have to place a
trap, gently scrape the soil to the side rather than dig into it.
This will not damage the tunnel.

believe it unless they see it with their own eyes. So, if possible, ensure
the customer is watching to authenticate your catch.

How to catch a live mole?

At some point you will asked to catch a live mole. I have been asked to
catch a live mole for television productions, and this is probably one of
the only reasons why anyone should want to catch a live mole. To catch
a live mole it is necessary to study the fox and how he makes a meal of
a mole. The ideal conditions are large molehills where the mole would
be either above ground level actually in the molehill pushing up soil, or
at least just under the ground directly below the spoil heap.

When you see the molehill move, that is the time to move towards it.
When it stops moving you also stop. This helps to hide the noise you
may make in your creep towards it. Again, when the molehill moves
you move until you are within striking range. Fox being light on its
feet does not have this problem, and its cat-like instincts give it an
advantage. Its hearing also helps with the movement. Like a cat, it can
hear the mole beneath the ground digging.

The strike for the mole depends on where the mole is. If mole is in a
molehill large enough for you to think it will be above the surface
pushing the soil, dive forwards and push the complete molehill away
from you. If you have been correct in your judgment, the mole will be
pushed out away from the vertical shaft in the soil and you can grasp
it. Beware of the bite! A fox would roll on the mole or pounce to kill it
– it is important not to hesitate as a mole will dig down and be out of
sight before you know it. Should the molehill be of a size that mole

TOP TIP

Should you open up the wrong run or find you have a junction, do not fill it in or cover it. Leave it open and let the mole close it up – which it will. Natural predators will often open up a tunnel, so the mole is well used to this disturbance. Remember then to set your trap away from this location, but possibly in a run linking to it.

will not be in the spoil and the ground is soft enough, the strike should be downward.

Leap forward with all the weight on the hands to pin the mole momentarily in the collapsed shaft or run. Have a small trowel ready and quickly but carefully dig down to catch the mole before it again disappears. I do not recommend you try this as it can cause unnecessary injury to the mole. When moles are running spooked they can be hooked out with a spade – the mole spud was often used for this.

I always feel that unless it is for a very good reason, then don't catch a live mole and avoid those who insist you do.

To catch a mole by the depth method

Another common problem is the mole running spooked in a well-tilled soil or flowerbed. Here in the loose soil the mole almost 'swims', and it can cause great damage to flowerbeds. It can be very frustrating to catch this mole, for the runs tend to collapse when setting the trap. In the event of this happening you need to use the depth method.

The trap needs to be set lower in the soil. This is best achieved using the half-barrel trap. The arched top of the trap is set almost half way down the diameter of the tunnel. Well-sifted soil is sprinkled over the trap to cover it. The amount of soil needed to cover the trap will not hamper the operation of the springs if the springs are new or maintained.

When the mole is running shallow, it is almost swimming in the soil. It is pushing the soil over its head and therefore dipping downwards as it moves forwards. This is carried out in soft soil and to catch the mole set a half-barrel trap down in the run so that the arch of the trap roof is actually in the run. The mole will thrust its self forwards and downwards into the trap.

When the mole is running spooked like this it will always ensure that a covering of soil is above it to protect it from attack by predators. The mole moving in these types of runs is slightly lower, pushing the soil over its head in a swimming action. The trap set lower will mean that mole dives low into the trap and is caught.

To stop a mole digging under a trap

Similar problems occur when the mole continues to dig under a trap even if light and moisture are excluded. The mole may have many reasons for this but, to over come the problem, place a natural hard substance under the trap. This will prevent the mole from digging down and cause mole to be caught.

Natural substances are best for this purpose, as a mole is used to digging around stone and roots. I buy the thin pieces of natural slate, which chip, and break off the large ornamental pieces – they are usually the right size and are very cheap.

TOP TIP
If you find a small hole has been dug down into the mole tunnels and is open, consider that a weasel may have entered in search of a meal. The hole will be obvious, and will have a small amount of soil scraped and piled next to it. If this happens, you may find the weasel and not the mole in the trap!

I still cannot find that run!

If you are still having trouble finding that hatched zone run and you are working quite deep, try this. Clear all the molehills away for two occasions and walk over the area – wait for the arrival of the first two or three new molehills, on the third occasion, probe down to find the run linking up your chosen two molehills. Cut into the run and set a half-barrel trap in the tunnel. When cutting the hole for the trap cut it about half an inch too small [15mm]. Push the trap down firmly into the run so it cuts its own path. Do not remove or clean any loose dirt out. Cover and check within twenty-four hours. This often works because the mole expects to have to remove some soil from the runs due to the disturbance you placed upon it in the previous two occasions. This works well in wet soil when the mole is working deep.

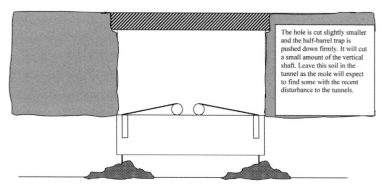

The hole is cut slightly smaller and the half-barrel trap is pushed down firmly. It will cut a small amount of the vertical shaft. Leave this soil in the tunnel as the mole will expect to find some with the recent disturbance to the tunnels.

I still cannot find that run!

The mole is under the patio

Sometimes the mole decides to dig under the patio or path. This is evident when the mole throws out dirt along the edges where a patio meets the lawn. As most paths or patios are laid on sand, moles often dig tunnels along this edge.

The problem is the difficulty in positioning the trap in the run and allowing the trap to operate fully. Here is my solution. Probe to find the run – you will have to enter at an angle – dig into the tunnel, set a half-barrel trap and enlarge the hole so that it lies on its side in the run. Ensure that the trap's arched roof lines up with the side of the mole run. This must be set correctly to outwit the mole. Often it is best to wait to see if the mole will venture out into the lawn to make an easier catch. If mole does enter the lawn, the trap must be set the same day mole ventures out.

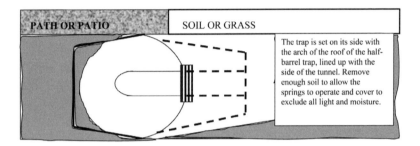

PATH OR PATIO   SOIL OR GRASS

The trap is set on its side with the arch of the roof of the half-barrel trap, lined up with the side of the tunnel. Remove enough soil to allow the springs to operate and cover to exclude all light and moisture.

The most difficult mole of all

Most moles are difficult to catch, that goes without saying, but the most difficult ones to catch are those that have chosen to move into mounds of soil or high banks. This usually occurs when the flat ground is wet. As I have already said, this mole is difficult to catch, so if it is possible to allow the mole to return to the flat ground when it becomes drier, then do.

The problem with banks and mounds is that the mole will, nine times out of ten, be in the middle pushing spoil out sideways and upwards. The obvious problem is the depth the mole will be working at. Mounds of loose soil will mean that it is difficult to probe these runs, and the tunnels will collapse if they are too loose. The answer is to probe

TOP TIP
In the breeding season a half-barrel trap can and often
will catch two moles at one time

slowly and try to establish a run. Mark the depth at which it was found on your probe. The trowel work will have to be slow and precise to cut down without causing any unnecessary damage, and in this is way it is an advantage to know the depth you have to dig. Having broken into the run, the sighting of the trap needs to be quick and the covering precise.

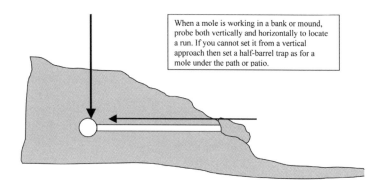

When a mole is working in a bank or mound, probe both vertically and horizontally to locate a run. If you cannot set it from a vertical approach then set a half-barrel trap as for a mole under the path or patio.

Mole spoil heaps found on the side of the bank or mound will probably have been pushed out sideways along a shaft. The probe will have to be pushed in horizontally, but depending on the location of the spoil, try probing from above. This will make it an easier trap site to work, as the trap can be set as normal. Should you have to enter horizontally, place as you would for a mole under a path or patio.

Moles in the breeding season

You will undoubtedly be asked to catch a mole when the breeding season is under way. This is always a busy time for the molecatcher, as the male moles moves around to find females, and the females will be digging to provide food whilst she is rearing her young.

A number of male moles may well be using the same tunnels to locate a female, possibly the same female. Should the call from a client to a mole problem reveal a single row of molehills, perhaps running along

TOP TIP

In spring, when breeding is under way, it is possible that other moles are using a territory. Once you have removed a resident mole, the client may call you back with new molehills. These moles may either be looking for a mate or just passing through. Your visits may prove fruitless if the mole has already moved on. So be prepared for this.

an edge of a flowerbed, patio or wall, then expect to be called back following the capture of a mole, especially if you first catch a male mole. It is under these circumstances that you always produce the mole to the client to avoid any confrontation later.

It is easy to predict mole's movements at this time of year. If moles are present in the surrounding areas, you can be confident that movement will occur. This is important information to pass on to your clients, as it will inform them that they may have to pay for another mole or moles to be removed from the same area.

It is also very important to consider the type of soil that you are working in at this time of the year. The males are not digging tunnels to create a feeding ground, they are only moving in a safe manner to fulfil their desire to mate.

At this time there is a good chance that the soil will be wet, and in heavy soil the mole will not remove much soil to the surface, but push and pack to make a smooth polished tunnel (which is well worth a look). The fact that they are in a frenzy to mate will mean a lot of movement down interlinking tunnels, so be confident of multiple catches. If you are catching over a wide area, such as a field, then stand back and view the whole location – there should be some single molehills between territories indicating where the linking tunnels are.

Locating a run

After conceiving, the females will begin to prepare for the forthcoming weeks by increasing their tunnels. The tell-tale sign here is a sudden increase in molehills in only a slightly larger territory. You can impress the client by predicting a female, and astonish them by producing her for payment.

These are only a few quick tips that should help you win over that elusive mole. There are many tried and tested tricks that as you progress, will become second nature.

Now I would like to mention molecatching on a farm, which is not always a task to relish

The farmer has a mole

Cow muck everywhere, biting winds and driving rain... still, the traps have to be checked. Agriculture waits still for no man, and should you

63

Mole caught in a trap

wish to attend a farm and undertake this venture, be warned that it is a hard task. Traps get trodden down into the ground, crushed by hoof and tyre, and traps go missing, but if you still you fancy it... here is some advice

1.   Explain the importance of a stock-free field until the work is completed.

2.   Mark the trap site with a hazel stick – the chances are that the grass will not have been cut for awhile.

3.   Ensure the grass will not be topped until you have finished.

4.   Only use a small number of traps and rotate the field – this will prevent large numbers of traps from being lost.

5.   Examine the soil and water table closely to see how the moles will behave.
6.   Look in the adjoining land.

7. Before taking on a task, calculate the number of possible moles you will have to remove. Consider the time of year and agree payment terms with the farmer.

8. Nail, tie or hang moles in full view of the landowner – make sure that they see your results. This is not always recommended when in public view.

9. Consider it again.

Summary

There have been times when I have not caught the mole because the phone call has occurred when the mole is merely passing through; it had gone before my arrival. As I only get paid for the moles I catch, this can mean that the only payment I get is a welcome cup of tea! Customers often wait until the last minute before calling in the molecatcher. Every conceivable piece of advice is tried before admitting defeat. This makes catching some moles a real challenge, because by the time you arrive the mole is conscious of someone or something trying to permanently oust it from this cozy haven.

The molecatcher has to be aware of every feature in the location and think like a mole to calculate the mole's movements. Then the traps have to be set perfectly, as this is inevitably the garden of the world's best cynic who constantly claims that his methods are the best and that you will not catch anything other then a cold. It is these jobs that call on every trick and little bit of knowledge molecatchers have tucked away.

I had a good job once catching moles at a stable. The moles had invaded the new-drilled paddocks. The numbers of mole runs and tunnels increased the risk of a horse damaging itsself by stumbling. Having cleared the area, I was then paid to keep it clear. Four traps kept it clear for a whole year. These were placed along and under the post and rail fence that bordered the paddocks, and caught moles well into double figures. (If you ever get a job like this, the fence line will normally catch every time.)

My quickest ever catch of a mole was at a doctor's house. I had just set the trap and covered it. Then as I stood up it sprung. I thought maybe the trap had released itself. I pulled it out with the mole firmly caught. The doctor was very impressed. However, I knew this mole was running in a straight line across the lawn, so if you get a job like this be prepared – work quietly and quickly and who knows, you too may make a quick catch!

The demands for molecatching come from all walks of life, and people do make the strangest requests. I was asked to catch a mole in a garden that was overlooked by a grand house. The lawns that ran down to a beautiful lake were bordered with herbaceous shrubs.

Mole had taken up residence in the lawn central to the view from the dining room. The gentleman had, over a period of time, been continually ribbed by his dinner guests about this mole. The glove was thrown down and the challenge (to be rid of the mole before the next dinner party) was accepted. The gentleman had tried hard to catch the mole, and the date of the next dinner party was approaching. He had no option but to call in help to win the wager. The guests never knew who really caught the mole.

Molecatching has taken me to many places, not only to catch moles but also to talk about them; these places include radio broadcasts, club talks and environmental meetings. This has given me the opportunity to meet many people and to hear their stories of molecatching. The numbers who have enrolled in the Jasper Carrot School of molecatching is enormous. Those who have heard of the comedian Jasper Carrot will be aware of the advice he was given in his hilarious sketch, 'The Mole'. Following the use of moth balls, smoke bombs and garlic, he resorted to an all night vigil with a shotgun, only to realize at the time of pulling the trigger that he had never fired a shotgun. This resulted in the premature removal of all the apples from his tree. People have laughed at this story for many years, but what they don't realize is that people will do anything to be rid of a mole.

I once met a very nice young lady who had received a Christmas card that when opened played the tune "We wish you a merry Christmas" continuously. She found the card particularly annoying, and so she buried it in the tunnel of the mole that was digging up her lawn. It obviously also got on the mole's nerves, as the mole just kept throwing it out. It didn't make the mole leave, however.

Health and safety

Mole catching has its risks – in 'Top tips' I referred to the importance of a good nail brush and nail clippers, and for very good reason – Clostridium. Clostridium is a bacteria found in soil of which there are many different species, including *Clostridium.Tetani*, which causes tetanus (lock jaw) in humans, and also *Clostridium Perfringens* which is responsible for severe diarrhoea. Others species can cause botulism or gangrene.

One reason for mole control is the damage to silage. This damage is caused when soil is harvested with the fodder and is fed to livestock. Listeria is the problem here, and it has the unusual ability to be able to grow at temperatures as low as 0°C, so the risk is ever present. There is no vaccine available to prevent this infection, although the infection can be treated with antibiotics. However, one-third of cases are fatal.

It is important to cover any wounds you might receive from sharp objects in the ground such as stones or glass, and ensure that your tetanus vaccination is current.

So my advice – other than do not bite your finger nails or pick your nose! – is get a good nail brush.

6

Molecatching in the modern world

Mole killers

Radio and television have featured people who claim to be molecatchers, and I have been anxiously waiting to hear and see the craft explained, only to be disappointed with no more than a 'mole killer.' Mole killer or molecatcher, there is little difference, many might say. But I feel there is a big difference! Mole killers cannot produce with the evidence of a mole they have completed the requested. Pest control companies will offer gassing as a control method. This is the application of pellet or powdered Aluminum Phosphide into the runs.

The gas, being heavier than air, floods the tunnel complex and kills the mole. We know that the mole has a good sense of smell, and this method may indeed work if the mole is confined in the area the gas has been applied to. But if the mole has sensed the disturbance, it is likely to have moved off to another area, or may not in fact be there, only entering that particular area in its quest for food. The gas last for about four to six hours, depending on the moisture content in the ground or atmosphere (which it needs to be activated). This gas will kill the worms and ground living grubs that the mole eats. It also may result in mole seeking an alternative location – until the treated ground recovers after the ordeal. Then the mole may return to its territory.

Should someone decide to employ a mole killer to gas the mole, then a word of warning. Gas cannot be used in close proximity to a building. A quick look at most modern gardens confirms that gas is quite often not an option.

Strychnine

It may seem strange after all I have said about the use of poisons that I include a piece on the awful stuff. I feel that to understand all there is to know about molecatching, it is necessary to also have some knowledge of the other methods of control that are used. The live tunnel traps I have already mentioned mentioned (and these may be the main competition to the molecatchers' traps in the future). The use of the deadly poison Strychnine has been responsible for many a molecatcher's demise.

The seed from the tree *Strcychnos nux vomica* is where the alkaloid extract comes from that makes Strychnine. Administered on worms placed in the runs of a mole, it produces the most painful death. A convulsion so fierce that the body almost snaps, but death is by hemorrhages in the lungs leading to asphyxia. In parts of America, the use of strychnine was prohibited due to the number of cases of accidental poisoning of pets. The risk of secondary poisoning has eventually been recognized in England, but also there is a risk to the person using this poison. A less toxic poison is Alphachloralose, a substance that has a hypnotic effect on animals, which leads to fatal hypothermia. It is used in place of strychnine in parts of Europe as it has no secondary poison risk.

Electronic devices

I mentioned earlier the electronic device, which has become a novelty in the world of mole control. Often, given such impressive names such as Mole scarer, or sonic molechasers, the manufacturers claim that, when planted in the ground, these simple devices will frighten away the moles by producing a subsonic vibration and sound that the moles interpret as predators. They claim they will remove the moles from an area of 1000 square meters. Do they work? Well, if the number of moles I am called to catch from areas where these devices have been installed is an indication, then they do not. I would not expect anyone to take my word for this. Well-educated people at a university in Scotland back in 1994 undertook some tests to see exactly what response these musical spikes had on moles. Moles fitted with radio transmitters had these devices placed in their territories; the results gave no indication to the moles being repelled by the mechanical devices. The Advertising Standards Authority asked the manufacturers to produce evidence of their effectiveness, but they have failed to do so thus far.

So would they work or not? Call me cynical – I can see the theory behind them, but in practice they will do just the opposite. Remember that the mole feels its environment through an acute nervous system stimulated by the hairs on its body and that sensitive nose. Vibrations mean one of two things to a mole – predation or food. It may well retreat a distance away for a short time, but with no predator actually coming through the tunnel complex, then the mole may think that the vibrations are food. Often you see the device surrounded by fresh molehills where the mole has increased a tunnel complex as a result of this vibration. These devices can encourage moles by the very action that the manufacturers claim deters them.

Worm charming is possibly the reason for this. It may not be quite an Olympic sport as yet, but its popularity in certain areas is growing. It does have its own world championships. The objective is to encourage as many worms from a square of land within a given time. During a competition, the only method that is accepted is the use of vibrations. The favoured method is to push a fork into the soil and cause vibrations down the prongs from trapping or banging another part of the fork. It is taken very seriously, and all manner of items are used to cause these vibrations – a notched piece of wood may be used to strike or 'fiddle' the handle of the fork to assist vibration.

America and molecatching around the world

Now I have never been to America, but I have had much communication regarding moles from 'across the pond'. I was very privileged when *Country Life* magazine published a feature article on me, labelling me as a 'National living treasure'. This article was read in a worldwide market, and I was surprised to start receiving letters from the United States. One chap actually asked if I would go to Virginia and catch his moles for him! He even offered to send me a ticket. Obviously, the temptation was there, but alas I had to decline. As a result of the article, I was very intrigued to receive a trap from one reader in America. It was a *Victor spear trap* – a copy of the old Guillotine trap of a hundred years ago. I was surprised that a country so far advanced still preferred a trap of the old style.

I enquired further and discovered a range of traps available to catch the various species of moles in the States. One molecatcher, Tom Schmidt, who I still correspond with, prefers them to our half-barrel traps. The biggest surprise of all was the sudden excitement over the English scissor trap, which many suppliers over there think is the best thing since the hot dog. Moles in the United States are much bigger than ours. The Hairy Tailed Mole and the Common or Eastern Mole frequent the Eastern United States. The widest spread is the Star Nosed Mole. The West Coast is home to four species of moles. The Broad Footed Mole, American Shrew Mole and the Coast Mole. The Townsend Mole is the largest of all of America's moles, and is now becoming a protected species in parts.

Mole control in the States is mainly by the use of traps, and prior to this new interest in English traps, they largely used three trap types.

The Victor Harpoon trap

This trap is the most commonly used, and is effectively the same as the guillotine trap of old. I feel that it is the humane way in which it quickly dispatches the mole in shallow runs that make it a favourite. It must be remembered that the depth at which it can be used is limited. Humane the harpoon trap may be, but obviously there are still those who feel the removal of a mole punctured by half a dozen 150mm nails can be somewhat messy. Therefore, also on the market is a *Choker* trap.

The Choker trap

The Choker Trap is also used in shallow runs. It consists of a spring, which pulls up two loops when the trigger is released. The principle is identical to our loop trap, only it is larger, with the bulk of the trap remaining above the ground and to the side of the run. It is again set like the harpoon trap, by flattening the top of a shallow run with a foot or hand; two slots are then made with the trowel to allow the loops to be pushed down into the run. When the mole enters the flattened tunnel and pushes up the roof, the trigger is released, allowing the spring to pull up the loops catching the mole.

The above two traps are effective – but somewhat grim – methods of control to be left in full view of the paying public.

The Out O'sight trap

The *Out O'sight* mole trap is hardly that as, like the previous two traps, it has a large spring and scissor jaws which require levers to force them apart to make it ready for use. This trap is almost identical to the Talpex trap, but can hardly be called the Out o' sight trap as, yes, you have guessed it, it is set in a shallow run and relies on the mole pushing up a flattened tunnel or the trigger to release it.

Other devices

A new device appearing on the Internet, and that could make its way to the UK, is the *Mole blaster*. It seems that our desperation to be rid of mole has now led us to employ explosives. The device is mainly available in France, Belgium and Italy, and uses small explosive charges that are placed in the run below a molehill. It relies on the fact that if you leave a molehill open, the mole will eventually come and close it by pushing earth up. The motion of pushing up the soil triggers an electric charge from a battery, which detonates the explosive charge. The trap has enough power in the charge to kill the mole.

I cannot believe that people will allow this method of control in their lawns.

Mole bulbs are used in Sweden, and will probably appear on the shelves almost anywhere. The bulbs apparently secrete an odour that conveniently humans cannot smell but keeps moles away.

7

The mole in the media

Moles have appeared in shops as novelty gifts and even garden ornaments. They are now even the main name behind a brewery. We have written stories based on the character of a mole, always as a funny, cuddly little creature with a smile on its face.

Molecatchers too have been the subject of literature. The famous tale of the *Molecatchers Daughter* was made into a film. This was the *Murder of Maria Marten*, the daughter of the molecatcher at Polstead, in Suffolk by one William Corder in 1827. The tragic tale was made into a film called *Murder in the Red Barn*.

Songs and ballads have also told of the plight of both moles and molecatcher. My favourite being a folk song aptly named *Molecatcher*.

MOLECATCHER

In Wellington town at the sign of the plough
There lived a molecatcher shall I tell you how

Chorus
Singing too-rel-I-day
Ful de lie lad-die lie, lad-die di day

He'd go a molecatching from morning to night
And a young fellow came for to play with his wife

The mole in the media

Chorus
Singing too-rel-I-day
Ful de lie lad-die lie, lad-die di day

The molecatcher jealous of this very same thing
He hid in the washhouse to see him come in

Chorus
Singing too-rel-I-day
Ful de lie lad-die lie, lad-die di day

He saw the young fellow come over the stile
Which caused the molecatcher, so crafty to smile

Chorus
Singing too-rel-I-day
Ful de lie lad-die lie, lad-die di day

He knocked on the door and thus he did say
Where is your husband, good woman I pray?

Chorus
Singing too-rel-I-day
Ful de lie lad-die lie, lad-die di day

He's gone a molecatching you need never fear
But little did she think the molecatcher was near

Chorus
Singing too-rel-I-day
Ful de lie lad-die lie, lad-die di day

She went up the stairs and gave him the sign
And the molecatcher followed them quickly behind

75

Molecatcher

Chorus
Singing too-rel-I-day
Ful de lie lad-die lie, lad-die di day

And while the fellow was up to his frolics
The molecatcher caught him quite fast by his bollocks

Chorus
Singing too-rel-I-day
Ful de lie lad-die lie, lad-die di day

The trap it squeezed tighter, which caused him to smile
Saying here's the best mole that I've caught in a while.

Chorus
Singing too-rel-I-day
Ful de lie lad-die lie, lad-die di day

I'll make you pay well for tilling my ground
And the money it'll cop you no less than ten pound

Chorus
Singing too-rel-I-day
Ful de lie lad-die lie, lad-die di day

Ten pound, says the young fellow, that I don't mind
It only works out about two pence a grind

Chorus
Singing too-rel-I-day
Ful de lie lad-die lie, lad-die di day

So come all young fellows and mind what your at
And don't get them caught in the molecatchers trap

Chorus
Singing too-rel-I-day
Ful de lie lad-die lie, lad-die di day

Those of you who may prefer the odd jig may wish to bop to the molecatcher's hornpipe.

8

The future for molecatching

From the very first time you catch mole, whether it be in your own garden or commercially, you never stop learning about mole. It is an understanding that will grow with each encounter. Take mole on as a commercial enterprise and beware, as the little man in black could be your ruin. I find that it is very important to be in the right frame of mind to catch a mole – going out to catch a mole with your personal attitude wrong – when you're feeling low or ill – will result in senseless mistakes and a failure to catch. You have to *want* to catch the mole, not just *have* to.

Mole numbers are increasing as the amount of land available to them is decreasing, reduced by man's development.

We will have to learn to live with moles, and to control their numbers. If it is to survive as a species, those who have the knowledge – molecatchers – can carry out this work. Modern technology may well strive to find some machine, computer or robot to carry out this task, but the mole has so far overcome all of these efforts. It is difficult to explain in words, but the understanding a man needs with a horse to form a team is similar to that we need with a mole if we are to catch it. An understanding no machine could ever achieve.

Molecatching to me is an essential service, and something I enjoy doing. It may well mean the taking of a life, but it also means the control of a species to furtherance its existence. The removal of a number of moles from an area means that the moles' competition for food is reduced until the next season.

I visit many countryside parks (often run by countryside rangers) who have areas plagued by moles. When asked how they control the numbers, the reply is they do not. Do not or cannot? Even in natural areas where man is the main control of predation, animals need to be controlled to a level that does not exceed the carrying capacity of the habitat, to reduce suffering in the competition for food. Molecatching is only a small part of the correct running of the countryside, and much of the work of the molecatcher is carried out in the gardens of new homes that have been bulit on a mole's territory.

If we are to share this world with all, we must learn to share it properly. We are the dominant race, and see ourselves as the ruling body, so surely to rule should ensure that all who come under this ruling are treated with notability and respect. If a life has to be removed for whatever reason, it should be carried out by whatever method is the most humane and causes least suffering.

The mole has been around for many years, and it will be around for many more. The quiet subterranean world it lives will change little, despite man's efforts above ground.

Now you have read a little of this mysterious world of the mole and the molecatcher, I hope you will understand the reasons why this most common yet rarely seen of mammals has plagued man for so long, and why a few have strived to catch them.

I cannot pretend my reason for catching moles it is for the four shillings any more .My wish is a simple one – to be MOLECATCHER by Royal Appointment, whatever rewards it brings. Well we all live in hope...

GOOD CATCHING!!